A National Tru

GW00360015

Battle for Britain

THE INSIDE STORY OF HILL FORTS

Harry T Sutton

BATSFORD – HERITAGE BOOKS

Illustrations: Chapter 1 and 2, Ken Kirkland;
Chapter 3, Moira Clinch

Copyright © 1979 by B T Batsford Limited and Heritage Books

Produced by Heritage Books, 36 Great Russell Street, London WC1B 3PP

Published jointly by B T Batsford Limited and Heritage Books

Distributed by B T Batsford Limited, 4 Fitzhardinge Street,
London W1H 0AH

Made and printed in Great Britain by
William Clowes & Sons Limited, Beccles, Suffolk

ISBN 0 7134 2119 3

Contents

1 The Fall of Mai Dun

The 2nd Augusta Legion had been on the march for three days and Julius Felix, a soldier in the 3rd Cohort, felt bad-tempered and tired.

'It beats me why we ever came to this benighted country in the first place,' he grumbled. 'There are no roads, no decent towns, no baths—and for that matter, there are no people either!'

A Centurion, riding along the marching column, heard the soldier's words. He turned in his saddle and recognised the speaker as one of the Legion's greatest grumblers. But Julius Felix, he knew, was a good soldier just the same.

'We shall meet people soon enough, don't you fear, soldier,' the Centurion said. 'The Britons put up a good fight when we crossed the river Thames and they are not all beaten yet. You may not have seen them for two or three days, but we may be attacked by thousands tomorrow!'

What he said was true. The first days of the invasion of Britain had not been easy. The enemy fought well, racing around in their two-wheeled chariots, hurling spears into the massed Roman ranks then dashing quickly out of arrow shot. Other Britons, hiding in bushes and trees, sniped at them with bows and arrows whilst javelin throwers darted from cover to hurl their deadly spears.

But Roman training and discipline had beaten the Britons at last, and the tribes of Kent and eastern Britain surrendered. Now the 2nd Legion, six thousand strong, was heading west into unknown parts where the natives were said to be especially brave and fierce.

'I beg your honour's pardon,' said Julius Felix, as the Centurion rode on down the column. Then he added, so that only his mates could hear—'You should be locked up, you old fool.

A cow in a field could make you shake with fear!'

And his companions laughed.

'He may be an old fool, but what he said is true enough,' said one. 'We shall soon meet the Wessex Britons — too soon for my liking!'

For another hour the Legion marched, the column stretching for a mile along the ancient trackway to the west. In the lead were archers and cavalry to deal with an attack from ahead; at the end of the column were infantry and more cavalry to repel attacks from the rear. Between were mules and oxcarts carrying heavy weapons, tents, trenching tools and all the equipment an army needs for war. Behind the main body of heavily armed soldiers rode the commander of the Legion, General Vespasian, and his staff.

The column travelled fast. Four Roman miles an hour was the normal pace and it was a relief to the weary men when at

last the order came to halt. Army surveyors went ahead to find a good place to camp and the troops gratefully broke ranks to rest in the rough grass beside the track.

'Who'd be a blessed soldier?' sighed Julius Felix as he unloaded the pack from his back. And this time none of his mates laughed. They all agreed.

A few miles to the west, the townsfolk of Mai Dun were returning from the fields, their day's work ended, unaware of the danger which was now so close. It was the year 43 A.D. and all Britain knew that a Roman army had landed somewhere along the south coast. There was news of battles fought and some of the British tribes, it was said, had surrendered and agreed to accept Roman rule. Word had come that troops were marching west and for weeks the town had prepared in case the Romans came that way. For Mai Dun was a fortress town. It's high earth and stone walls were built to protect the people from just such an enemy attack.

Great stocks of slingstones had been collected from the seashore and stacked along the ramparts where they would be ready to hand; the banks and ditches round the town were repaired and strengthened where rain and frost had worn them down; tree trunks were dragged to the great entrance gates to block them against the enemy. The people of Mai Dun were determined to be ready should the Romans try to take their town.

But on that fine, warm evening as the farmers made their slow way home, nobody worried about the Romans or the danger to Mai Dun. The men sang cheerful country songs as they strolled along; the women gossiped together and the children ran ahead, playing games of 'he' and 'catch-as-catch-can'. There was danger, of course, for the Romans would surely come. But the sun was warm, the day's work was done and it was good to enjoy life while they could.

On a sunny bank beside a field, two children and an aged man lingered behind the rest. Hugh the Gaul was fifty-five and too old for work. He was the oldest man in Mai Dun and in his long life had seen many strange things. He was a great

favourite with all the children of the town who loved to hear him talk.

Dai and Olwen, brother and sister, who sat with him now in the evening sun, were his especial friends.

'Tell us about when you lived in Gaul,' begged Dai.

'Yes,' added Olwen. 'And how the Romans took the people to be slaves!'

Hugh the Gaul looked sad. 'The Romans set fire to our town and took the young men away to be their slaves.' A tear ran down his ancient, wrinkled face. 'Only the old men and the women and children were spared. All who resisted were killed.'

'Was that when you came to live at Mai Dun?' asked Olwen.

'Yes,' said the old man. 'With some of my friends I escaped and crossed the sea to Britain. I was only a lad then but I was a champion slinger – and we Gauls are famous for our skill with the sling. I taught the men of Mai Dun the Gallic way to sling.' The old man paused and pointed across the field, to where some birds had settled amongst the crops. 'Let me see, boy, what you can do,' he said to Dai.

All the boys of the town learned to use the sling by firing stones at birds to scare them away from the crops and Dai now took his sling and picked up a stone. Taking aim he whirled the leather sling round his head and loosed the missile at the birds. It was a good shot and although he did not hit them, the birds flew off and Dai sat down again.

'Well done,' said Hugh the Gaul.

'Show us how you can hit a stick with a slingstone, half a field away,' Dai now asked him. But the old man was not so easily persuaded. It was warm and comfortable resting in the sun and to sling a stone, he would have to stand up. 'Not now,' he said.

But Olwen joined her brother with: 'Please, old Hugh, show us how you can hit a stick!' And because Gauls can never say 'no' to a pretty girl, the old man got slowly to his feet. Then he untied the long leather sling which he always carried as a belt round his waist.

10

'Choose a stone for me then, Dai,' said Hugh. 'Smooth and round—and heavy enough, mind! And set up a stick for a....' Suddenly he broke off and, shielding his eyes, he stared into the distance.

'Be still,' he said. 'And quiet!' Then, bending low, he beckoned Dai and Olwen to follow him.

'Romans!' he exclaimed, in a hushed voice.

Down the field-side, crouching low behind the corn; along a ditch and into some bushes he led them. There he stopped and the three lay hidden, watching the track nearby.

In the distance there came the sound of horses' hooves. Looking up at the old Gaul, Dai saw a grim look on his face. In one gnarled hand he held his sling; in the other a heavy stone.

Two more stones were beside him on the ground. Dai, too prepared his sling. They waited, silent and tense.

Voices could now be heard, and the chink of harness as the riders came near. Soon Dai and Olwen saw them clearly — two Roman officers in splendid armour, shining helmets and breast-plates; swords at their sides.

They were but a few paces away when Hugh stood up. His sling whirled just once above his head. A stone flew and one of the Romans lurched sideways from his horse and fell to the ground. The other reined in furiously, drew his sword, and moved towards the bushes. But the old man had chosen his position well. As the Roman turned he looked full into the evening sun and did not see that long sling whirl once more. Nor did he feel at first the stone that hit his arm, splintering the bone and sending his sword clattering to the ground. He looked fearfully at the blood showing crimson below his sleeve, then, spurring his horse, he galloped off, leaving his companion to his fate.

That was quickly decided.

'One more job to be done,' said Hugh the Gaul. And picking up the sword, he strode to where the Roman officer lay unconscious on the ground. With one fierce thrust, he plunged the sharp blade into his enemy's throat.

'Come,' he said to the two frightened children. 'There is never smoke without fire. The Roman army cannot be far away and we must warn Mai Dun!'

General Vespasian stared at the wounded Centurion with disbelief.

'A great fortress, you say?' he asked. 'And ambushes set along every path and track?'

'Aye, my lord,' answered the man. 'My wounded arm is proof of my words for my companion was killed and I narrowly escaped with my life!'

'By how many Britons were you attacked?' asked one of the General's staff.

'There were a hundred, sir,' said the Centurion. 'Perhaps more. It was difficult to be sure for they fought with the sun

behind them and it was low in the sky...'

General Vespasian laughed. 'Then you should have outflanked them, man, turned them to put the sun in their eyes!' Then he waved his hand in dismissal. 'But go and get treatment for your arm,' he told him, 'and tomorrow we shall see for ourselves this great fortress for which you have such respect!'

Then he turned to his staff officers.

'It will be a wonder indeed,' he said, 'if in this uncivilised land we find a fortress to withstand our artillery and battering-rams!'

'Yes, indeed, my lord,' they replied, laughing. For the idea really was absurd.

'We must be prepared just the same,' said Vespasian. And his voice was serious. 'I am told these Wessex tribes are determined to resist.' Then, turning to the Adjutant, he said: 'Let the order be given. We march at dawn!'

The meeting house at Mai Dun was filled to the doors as people crowded in to hear the news. The Elders of the town were seated on the bench from which, on council days, they made the law. Before them, his famous sling still in his hand, stood Hugh the Gaul. The Chief among the Elders called for silence. Then he spoke to Hugh.

'They were Centurions?' he asked. 'Are you sure?'

'Aye,' answered Hugh. 'They were Centurions all right – they wore helmets and breastplates far better than any common soldier would wear.'

'They must have been scouting ahead,' said one of the Elders.

'Which means the Roman army is not far behind!' said another.

The Chief Elder nodded. 'Hugh killed one of them but the other escaped. By now the Roman commander will have heard about Mai Dun and tomorrow they will be at our gates!'

He rose from the Elders' bench and walked across to Hugh

the Gaul.

'You have done well,' he said. 'We are warned in time.' Then he turned to the others of his Council.

'Block the entrances,' he ordered. 'Post men to watch all along the walls. Tonight we shall make sacrifice to our gods and pray for victory!'

Late into the night, torches glowed dimly along the battlements as guards patrolled the walls. Horns blared their warlike sounds as two thousand warriors prepared themselves for war. Goats were slaughtered for sacrifice to the gods and blood was smeared upon swords and slings to give them magic powers.

At the holy place a fire blazed before the altar and in its gloomy light, priests turned and leaped in ritual dances whilst a thousand voices chanted prayers.

As night drew on the sounds grew fainter. The altar fire died down and people went through the cold darkness to their homes. Soon there was silence broken only by low cries of 'all's well' from the watchers on the walls and the sad hooting of owls hunting in the night.

Five thousand Britons slept uneasily in the threatened town. None knew what dawn would bring. For some, that dawn would surely be their last.

General Vespasian stopped his horse and stared with amazement at the fortress on the hill.

'Just look at it!' he exclaimed. 'Look at the size of the place!' The Adjutant to the Legion, riding by his side, was astonished too.

'We never saw a greater in Germany, nor in Gaul,' he agreed. 'It will not be easy to destroy.'

'If the Britons fight, that is,' said Vespasian. 'They may have no stomachs for Roman swords!'

'They have fought well enough up to now,' the Adjutant reminded him. 'And the Wessex tribes are more hostile. There are traitorous Gauls among them who have taught the Britons to hate us — and taught them too, the Gallic way to fight.'

The General looked thoughtful.

'The famous slingers of Gaul,' he said. 'Do you think we shall once more have to fight against the sling?'

'Yes, General,' said the Adjutant. 'And by the look of that fortress, two or three thousand of them at the very least!'

'Let us test them then,' the General said. 'Let us see if you are right.'

Turning to his staff officers he gave orders for the battle to commence.

'Send the first Cohort to attack the eastern gate. The second Cohort to attack the walls on either side. Keep the third and fourth Cohorts in reserve. Give those orders and we shall see what appetite these Britons really have for war!'

The six Cohorts of the Legion were halted along the rough track which led to Mai Dun and to these the staff officers now rode, passing on the General's orders for the attack. The well-drilled lines of men, each Cohort more than a thousand strong, divided at once. Two Cohorts marched directly to Mai Dun;

the rest remained behind, ready to join battle should the order come.

Julius Felix was not among the advancing troops. He was a loader with a battery of catapults which, with the ballistae, were the long range artillery of the Legion. As the infantry went forward to test the strength of the defence, Julius helped to unload his catapult which, broken down into separate parts, was carried on the backs of several mules.

The artillery Centurion had chosen a good place for the big siege weapons. There was flat ground directly in line with the eastern entrance to the fortress, about two hundred metres away, and soon there would be twelve weapons in position, ready to fire.

Watching beside his catapult, Julius could hear the shouts of sergeants and corporals calling the step for the columns as they marched along the rough track that led to Mai Dun. 'Left-right, left-right, left-right, left!' they called, and the long lines of men moved steadily forward as if on a ceremonial parade. Many times Julius Felix had seen them advance in Germany and Spain, but never before had it seemed quite as impressive as this. It was hard to believe that those marching columns, dwarfed by the great fortress before them, could break through those well-protected walls. Yet he knew exactly how it would be done.

Soon, he knew, the leading column would reach the gates. They might be fired on by bows and arrows and a few spears on the way, but their shields and armour would protect them from that. The officer would demand entrance in the Emperor's name and then, if they were sensible, the Britons would open the gates. A payment in gold would be taken as tribute and the best of the men and women made slaves. There might be some loot to be shared out amongst the troops. Then the Legion would move on. That had been the pattern all through Britain once the first hard battles of the invasion had been won. And Julius Felix could see no reason why it should be different now.

But then, as he watched, a horn sounded from the fortress walls. Just as the leading Roman column reached the maze of defence ditches leading to the entrance, hundreds of men

suddenly appeared, running along the steep banks outside the
town. A few of them wore armour and helmets but most were
bareheaded with only tough leather jerkins to protect them.
But they all carried swords and slings.

'A reception party!' laughed one of the artillerymen. 'Our
lads will soon deal with them.'

But it was not to be so simply done. The Britons began a
bombardment of slingstones, so fierce that it brought the Roman
column to a halt.

The Romans had a battle formation which they called the
'tortoise', and the officers gave the order for it now. Each man
moved his left arm, on which he wore his shield, from a position
in front of his body to one in which the shield was carried horizon-
tally above his head. With their shields in this position the column
advanced once more, protected from slingshots by the tortoise-
like shell above their heads.

Seeing this, the slingers on the outposts redoubled their attacks. Aiming their missiles low, they were able to hit the advancing soldiers on their arms and legs. Gaps began to appear in the Roman ranks as men were killed by the fierce attack.

Archers among the advanced column were now ordered to fire at the slingers, but their bows were not powerful enough. Their arrows fell short and the rain of stone went on.

Then, a trumpet sounded from the Roman lines. It was the General's order for the two Cohorts to withdraw and, as the men turned back, a great roar of triumph went up from the walls of Mai Dun.

'They're cheering too soon!' said one of the artillerymen.

'Aye,' agreed Julius Felix. 'It will be our turn next!'

For two whole days the people of Mai Dun watched the Romans preparing for another attack. Standing beside Hugh the Gaul

on the battlements, Dai and Olwen could clearly see the Roman camp. Where only yesterday there had been cornfields there were now a thousand tents of leather arranged neatly in precise rows. Round the camp there was a ditch and a fence along which sentries patrolled by day and night. Smoke rose from cooking fires and, even though it was a mile away, the noise of work inside the camp could be clearly heard. Shouted orders and the tramp of marching men; blacksmiths' hammers forging weapons for the battle still to come; the shrill notes of trumpeters calling soldiers to duties or to food. And all day long they saw parties of men setting off across the countryside to return with loads of heavy stones which, Hugh said, would soon be hurled against Mai Dun.

'But how can that be?' asked Dai. 'No sling could throw stones as big as that.' And Hugh pointed to the row of strange-looking machines lined up facing the entrance to the town.

'Once I saw things like those in Gaul,' he told the boy. 'They throw stones — and javelins. The Romans used them against forts in Gaul and when the battle starts they will surely be used against Mai Dun!'

Then they saw the Romans fell a tree, a great oak which had stood for a hundred years upon a nearby hill. Its branches were removed as the children watched and the trunk was mounted within a wooden frame which moved on wheels.

'A battering-ram!' said Hugh the Gaul. 'I have seen them too! They will use that, if we cannot stop them, to break down the town gates!'

'What is to be done?' asked Dai. And for the first time he felt afraid. 'How *can* we stop them?'

Slowly the old man untied the sling from about his waist.

'This old sling may still have one last job to do!' he said. And his voice was firm; his eyes were bright. To the watching

children, at that moment, he did not look old at all.

The bombardment began at dawn. Inside Mai Dun, stones bigger than a man's fist began to fall amongst the flimsy wooden huts, killing many as they slept, and wounding others running for safety through the town. Blazing javelins hurtled over the walls to fall on the straw-thatched roofs and soon many houses were on fire.

The only safety to be found was in the shelter of the high ramparts where Olwen and Dai's mother now led them. But there was too much to be done for them to remain there long. There were wounded to help; baskets of slingstones to carry; the dead to be dragged from the ramparts to a place where they could be left until there was time for burial.

Too old to fight, Hugh the Gaul seemed to be everywhere at once, directing the women and children and the other old men in the work of helping the slingers who were fighting and dying to save Mai Dun.

The Romans were once more concentrating all their efforts on the eastern end of the town, but this time, instead of advancing on the gates, the assault was aimed at the walls themselves. Thousands of soldiers attacked across the wide banks and ditches outside the main rampart, warding off slingstones with their shields while the artillery sent a continuous barrage of stones and javelins over their heads against the defenders on the walls.

As the attack grew in strength, more and more Britons ran to the threatened place to hold the Romans off. Soon, all the defenders were gathered there — leaving the rest of the ramparts deserted.

Hugh the Gaul saw the danger at once.

'Come', he said to Dai. And the two of them ran to a place where they could climb through the fence which surrounded the town, and on to the rampart itself.

'There!' shouted Hugh, above the din of battle, pointing to where a large force of Roman soldiers was advancing along the road which wound through the outer defences to the main entrance gates. In the middle of the column, hauled by more than a hundred men, was the battering-ram!

'It must not reach the gates!' said Hugh, his face grey with anxiety. Then, followed by the boy, he ran as fast as his aged legs could carry him, towards the ramparts above the gates.

'We must hold them off!' he gasped, as they ran.

'I will help!' cried Dai.

As he helped to turn the windlass to reload his catapult, Julius Felix had time between each shot to watch the battle unfold. The great stones fired by the ballistae smashed against the ramparts of the fort, sending showers of earth into the air where they hit and cutting down the defenders like corn before the scythe. The catapults were shooting their javelins at slingers attacking from the flanks — running along the top of the outer ditch in a desperate attempt to turn the Romans away from the main rampart.

Approaching the eastern gate, the battering-ram with the fourth Cohort in support, continued its slow journey through

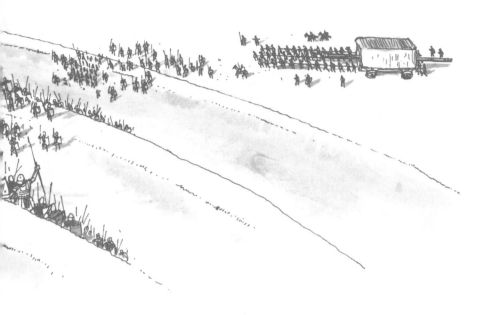

the twisting entrance defences, meeting no opposition on the way.

Julius turned to watch the soldiers fighting in the ditches; then he looked up at the ramparts above, crowded with every fighting man the town could raise. And Julius laughed.

'Old Vespasian is a clever one,' he muttered as he prepared the catapult for another shot. 'He has drawn the enemy away from the gates and there is nothing now to stop the battering-ram!'

But then he looked again. High up on the rampart above the gates, two figures had appeared. One was tall, an old man but of powerful build. The other was smaller. A boy, surely, not more than twelve years old. As he watched, they began to attack the men hauling the battering-ram with a bombardment of slingstones.

'It cannot be possible!' said Julius Felix, in amazement.

But it was possible. Out of range of the Roman archers, the

two slingers were keeping up a rapid fire, their height giving their slingstones added weight. That their fire was accurate was obvious for already there were men falling by the roadside. And where they fell they remained — unconscious or dead.

For a time the battering-ram was pressed forward, but it was now in the narrow passage which led to the gates and the two slingers had a target which they could hit again and again. Time after time their slings whirled and stones flew straight and true. Man after man fell before their furious attack. And the battering-ram came to a halt.

It was absurd! Julius Felix simply could not believe it. Two slingers, mere tribesmen, holding up the Legion!

It was soon clear that General Vespasian was also surprised by this setback to his plan. He galloped up to the artillery lines on his charger and shouted to the Centurion:

'Clear the gateway defences!' Then he pointed to the two lone defenders above the gates. 'Get rid of those two slingers!' he ordered.

Four catapults ceased their fire against the ramparts. The artillerymen swung their heavy weapons. They trained their sights on the two solitary figures above the gates.

'Fire!' shouted the Centurion in charge of artillery.

Dai and Hugh battled on. The pile of slingstones beside them would soon run out for the two were fighting desperately. Their bombardment could not have been equalled by four men, so fast did they shoot.

'The leader—Hugh! Strike the leader!' Dai shouted as the huge battering-ram lurched forward again on its heavy wheels.

'Aim low, beneath their shields!' cried Hugh the Gaul, his

voice hoarse with exhaustion.

When they saw the battering-ram stop, the two rested their tired arms for a moment. But then Hugh saw how few slingstones were left and he turned anxiously to Dai.

'Fetch more stones — more stones!' he told him, urgently.

But it was too late. Even as he spoke, a javelin fired from one of the distant catapults flew between them and broke its point against the stonework of the wall behind.

Then another flew its deadly course and with horror Dai saw it bury its length in the brave heart of Hugh the Gaul. His right arm raised in the very act of slinging a stone at his hated enemy, the old warrior fell dead.

For a time Dai fought on alone. Stone after stone flew from his whirling sling to strike the Romans down below. But then at last, another javelin found its mark.

And the battering-ram lumbered on towards the gate.

Julius Felix marched into Mai Dun with the victorious Legion, trumpets sounding and standards flying high. Inside the town, scenes of death and destruction were everywhere. Angered by the fierceness of the defence, some of the first soldiers to break into the town had mercilessly slaughtered all who dared to bar their way. Men, women and children lay dead in the ruins of their homes. Among them were Olwen and her mother who had stood defiant to the last.

But by nightfall it was all over and the survivors began the sad task of burying the dead. All through the night the groans of the dying mingled with the sad cries of those who mourned for those they had lost in the bitter fight.

At dawn next day, sickened by the smell of death inside the town, Julius strolled out through the ruined gates. Remembering the brave defence of the two lone slingers, he made his way to the rampart where they had made their last stand.

As he came near the place, Julius saw another figure, only just visible in the early light. It was an officer and Julius was about to turn away when the man spoke to him. He was looking down at the two crumpled figures, Hugh the Gaul with Dai lying dead at his side. Javelins were embedded in their bodies, and both still grasped their slings in death-cold hands.

'You too admired their courage, soldier,' said the officer. And Julius saw it was General Vespasian himself who spoke.

'Yes, sir,' replied Julius, 'They were indeed a brave pair.'

'It was a pity they had to die,' said Vespasian. 'They would have made excellent slaves.'

2 The Inside Story

If, during a picnic in the country you dropped a coin from your pocket or purse, it could be very hard to find. It would sink down into the grass and be difficult to see. If you returned to the same place a year later, the coin might be completely covered up. Worm casts would have been thrown up from the earth below; grass would have grown over it; dust would have been blown by the wind to settle on top. You would never find your coin now.

Ten years later, the coin would probably be several centimetres below ground. Now, you would have to dig to find it. And that is exactly what archaeologists have to do when they look for clues to things that happened in the past.

All over Britain there are banks and ditches round the tops of hills which are all that is left of what were once hill forts like Mai Dun. Many have now been explored by archaeologists. The earth which has collected on top has been dug away and the original ramparts and walls have been found. One of the first to be thoroughly explored was Maiden Castle in Dorset. It is thought that it was probably called 'Mai Dun' in ancient times and it is, or course, the fort upon which the story in chapter one is based.

When the earth which now covers Maiden Castle was dug away, many traces of the battle against the Romans were found. There was a skeleton with a javelin still embedded in its spine; there were deep cuts in many of the skulls found where the Britons had been killed by Roman swords; huge piles of slingstones were found; and the main gates and part of the walls had been torn down by the Romans to prevent the fort from ever being defended again. There were ashes where houses had been burned to the ground. Roman coins were found, dating back to about the year 43 A.D. They could have been lost by Roman soldiers after their attack on the town.

There are more than 2,000 hill forts in Britain. Now we

come to the Inside Story of how and why they were built.

BUILDING A FORT

Imagine yourself an Ancient Briton. Together with other families of farmers, you have found a good place to live and farm. Now you need a fort for protection from unfriendly tribes. The only tools you have are picks made of antler-horn, shovels made from the shoulder blades of oxen, and baskets in which to carry earth.

There is a hill nearby and there you decide to build your fort. With your family and the others who have decided to join you — say 300 people altogether, you start work. The sides of the hills are not steep enough to prevent people from climbing up so first you must make the slopes much steeper by digging a deep ditch all round,

like this. The earth and rubble you dig from the ditch must be carried up to the top to be used to build a rampart round the top. If you find stone then that can be used to build a dry-stone wall round the top, like this.

If you cannot find enough stone, you will have to make your rampart of earth alone. You will first have to build a strong wooden fence which is called a revetment

like this. Then you pile the earth up behind it to make the rampart walk. If the earth you dug from the ditch is not enough you will have to quarry some from inside the fort. This will be a good idea for you will need to make flat places for the houses and you can use that earth for the ramparts.

Now you will have to make an entrance to your fort. You must make it as difficult as possible for an enemy to get close enough to burn down the gates or push them in with a battering-ram. If you simply built a gate into the rampart with a direct approach to it, the enemy would be able to rush straight to it before he could be stopped. The way to the gates must therefore be made to turn between high banks along which defenders can run to shoot at the enemy on the way.

Like this. There is one last thing you can do to complete the fort. Bows and arrows were not good weapons in those times for nobody had yet discovered how to make a really powerful bow. A good slinger could easily outshoot an archer. If you now dig another ditch outside the one already made, you will keep the enemy further away and whilst you will be out of range of his bowmen, your slingers will be able to reach him with their slingstones. It is believed that the outer ditches at Maiden Castle and at other hill forts, were added when Britons discovered how to use the sling. They were most probably taught by the Gauls.

This is how your completed fort might have looked.

Not all hill forts were built like that. Some were built on the top of hills which fell away to sheer cliffs on one or more sides. Then there was no need to build ramparts all round. Many forts of this type were built along the coasts. They are called 'promontory' forts and they look like this.

BRITAIN WHEN THE FORTS WERE BUILT

All hill forts were built for protection. At first, perhaps only to protect farmers and their herds of sheep or cattle from wild animals. Later, as the population grew, there were probably quarrels over ownership of land which led to war between tribes. Forts were then needed for sheer survival. They were brutal times and even if they survived the warfare, people's lives were very short. In one cemetery at Maiden Castle thirty-five skeletons were found and of these, eleven were those of infants. The oldest man buried there was only 55 when he died.

Most of the people were farmers, growing crops where the soil was good and herding cattle and sheep where the pastures were best. Most of the farmers and their families must have lived inside a hill fort or near enough to one so that if danger threatened, they could move quickly inside.

Life must have been rather like the days of cowboys and Red Indians, cattle rustlers and horse-thieves, in the American mid-West. But without the United States cavalry to come galloping to the rescue!

3 Where to see Hill Forts

There are so many hill forts in Britain that almost everybody lives within a few miles of one. Some have been worn down by the passing years or even ploughed up so that almost all signs of them have gone. Others are so overgrown with bushes or trees that they are hard to find.

There are plenty left, however, which have not been disturbed since Roman times. Standing within their earth walls now it is easy to imagine those long-passed days when tribe fought tribe and the Romans came at last to bring 300 years of peace. Stand on the ramparts and look down. It is easy to understand how with slingstones and swords, the defenders felt safe from attack. Stand below and look up and you will see why the Romans needed artillery to break the defence.

Many of the best hill forts now belong to the National Trust. They care for them and keep them unspoiled for us to visit.

Highdown Hill

Little Solsbury

Good places for picnics now; but scenes of bitter fighting and sudden death when those grass-covered banks were first dug.

Here now is a list of hill forts cared for by the National Trust. If there are any near where you live or where you go for your holidays, try to visit one and take this book with you; it will help you to understand how the fort must have looked when it was first built.

AVON
Cadbury Camp, nr Clevedon
There is a fine hill fort here, right on the coast.
Little Solsbury, nr Bath
This is a flat hilltop with a fine hill fort. The ramparts are faced with stone. The fort was excavated by the University of Bristol and the things they found are in the University Museum.

The Dodman

BUCKINGHAMSHIRE
Ivinghoe Beacon, nr Berkhamsted
This is one of the oldest hill forts in Britain. Weather has eroded away most of the defences but the line of the ramparts can still be seen as a terrace below which the hillside gets steeper. The original rampart was made of chalk rubble with timber revetments in front and behind.

CORNWALL
Cadsonbury, nr New Bridge
This well preserved hill fort is on top of a steep, isolated hill in the valley of the River Lynher. It has never been excavated and has been undisturbed from the time it was built, probably 300-500 B.C. There is a footpath from the nearby road.
The Dodman, nr Mevagissey
This is a promontory fort high up on the point south of

Mevagissey. You can get to it along a footpath from Penare or over the cliff path from Hemmick to Lamledra.

Maen Castle, nr Land's End

This fine promontory fort has a single wall, 60 metres long and 3.5 metres wide, protecting it from the landward side. The entrance can still be seen. It was through a walled passage about 2 metres wide and post holes were found at the entrance for wooden gates. An earthenware pot found there can be dated to about 300 B.C.

Trelissick, nr Truro

There is a well preserved promontory fort at Round Wood at the entrance to Cowlands Creek.

Treen Castle, nr Land's End

This is a promontory fort with small defensive ditches. Nearby is the famous Logan rocking stone.

Trencrom Hill, nr St. Ives

This fine hill fort has stone walls and the foundations of the original huts where the inhabitants lived can still be seen inside it. A history of the fort can be bought from the cafe nearby.

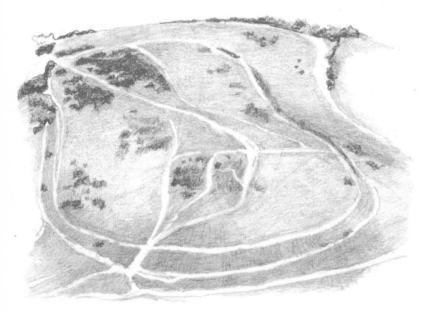

Cissbury Ring

DEVON
Hembury Castle, nr Buckfastleigh
This hill fort was excavated between 1930 and 1935. It was found that the inner bank was built from earth quarried from the ditch that runs round it inside the fort, and there was a palisade of close-set posts outside. Later, a second bank and ditch was added to give more protection. The gateways can still be seen.

GLOUCESTERSHIRE
Haresfield Beacon, nr Stroud
This is a promontory fort, 713 feet high. There are fine views from it over the Severn Valley.
Crickley Hill, nr Gloucester
There is part of a promontory fort on Crickley Hill with views over the Severn Valley.

HEREFORD AND WORCESTER
Croft Ambrey, nr Leominster
This hill fort was recently excavated. The site is a long narrow

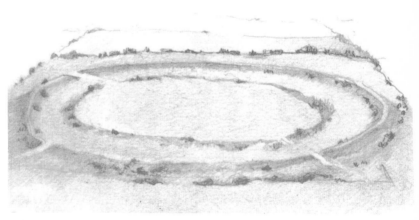

Figsbury Ring

Midsummer Hill

hill with steep slopes on both sides. There is one rampart which was once 12 metres high with a fence along the top. Inside, and along the full length of the wall, there were streets of small, four-post houses. They were laid out in straight rows like a modern housing estate.

Midsummer Hill, nr Ledbury
A hill fort on one of the Malvern Hills. Inside the fort the sites of several huts can be seen.

OXFORDSHIRE
Badbury Hill, nr Coleshill
A hill fort from which there are fine views over the upper Thames valley.

SOMERSET
Brean Down, nr Weston-Super-Mare
This is a headland on the coast, 300 feet high. At the point

there is a small promontory fort and around it the outlines of the fields farmed by the people who used the fort, can still be seen.

WEST SUSSEX
Cissbury Ring, nr Worthing
When this hill fort was excavated, many slingstones were found. The inside was ploughed during Roman times and a small cottage was built there. There are deep pits in parts of the fort. These were flint mines and are, of course, much older than the rest of the fort.
Highdown Hill, nr Worthing
This hill fort was built on top of an earlier settlement and a Saxon cemetery was found there during excavations. The finds are in Worthing Museum.

WILTSHIRE
Cley Hill, nr Warminster
The hill fort is on top of a chalk hill 800 feet high. There are two Stone Age burial mounds inside the fort.
Figsbury Ring, nr Salisbury
There are views over Salisbury from the top of this hill fort. The finds from the excavations and more information about the fort are in Devizes Museum.

MAP OF NATIONAL TRUST
HILL FORTS

☒ Hill Forts

Croft
Ambrey
            Crickley
Midsummer   Hill
Hill
Haresfield   Ivinghoe
Beacon   Beacon
            Badbury
Cadbury Camp   Hill
            Little Solsbury
Brean
Down   Figsbury
    Cley Hill   Ring
                    Cissbury
                    Ring
Hembury
Castle   Highdown
Cadsonbury   Hill
Trelissick
en
stle   The Dodman
Trencrom
Hill
Treen
Castle